The Letters go to hospital

by Roger Knights

The Lettermen were climbing a tree in their garden.

climb

fall

Oh dear!

As they climbed down, some of the Lettermen slipped and hurt themselves.

The other Lettermen called a doctor. He decided that the injured Lettermen must go straight to the hospital.

doctor

call

They ran to the telephone and called an ambulance, which arrived very quickly.

hospital

With its lights flashing and its siren wailing, the ambulance took the Lettermen straight to the hospital.

First, they had to have
an X-ray to see if any
bones were broken.

x-ray

Looking inside their bodies, they could see that they didn't have any broken bones.

look

bandage

Some of them had to
have bandages put
on their legs which
made them feel funny.

bed

After that, they were sent straight to bed for lots of rest!

A nurse took their temperature.

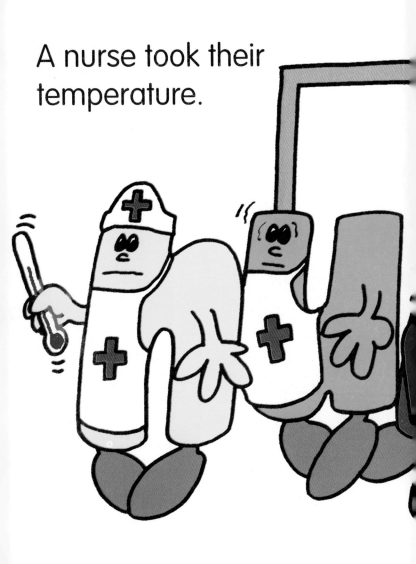

nurse

pills

She gave them lots of
different coloured pills
to take...one at a time!

The Lettermen couldn't sit
still for long.
They were soon bored.

bored

better

Soon, they started to feel much better.

When the nurse took off
their bandages they were
very pleased.
The bandages were hot
and itchy to wear.

Even though they could leave the hospital, they still had to walk with a stick for at least a week.

And guess where they went?

walk